This book is dedicated to

THINKING

Unfortunately, most of man's thinking is in *black* and *white* and rarely ever gets into the

gray matter.

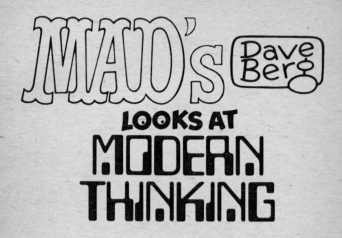

MAD's Dave Berg
LOOKS AT
MODERN
THINKING

WRITTEN AND ILLUSTRATED BY
DAVE BERG

EDITED BY ALBERT B. FELDSTEIN

Foreword by
Jerry De Fuccio

WARNER BOOKS

A Warner Communications Company

WARNER BOOKS EDITION
First Printing: August, 1976

Copyright © 1969 and 1976 by Dave Berg
and E.C. Publications, Inc.

This Warner Books Edition is published by
arrangement with E.C. Publications, Inc.

Warner Books, Inc., 75 Rockefeller Plaza, New York, N.Y. 10019

Ⓦ A Warner Communications Company

Printed in the United States of America

Not associated with Warner Press, Inc, of Anderson, Indiana

FOREWORD . . . MARCH!

Dave Berg was a war correspondent.

Though he received his honorable discharge long ago, Dave still engages in everyday conflicts and continues the war of nerves, yours and ours.

Dave says that life is a beachhead, so you must establish it!

Dave says life is taking the high ground, so you must rise to it!

Dave says life is a rear guard action, so you must go out gracefully!

Yes, Dave Berg is still a war correspondent.

Joyce Kilmer, he's not!

Jerry De Fuccio

Jerry De Fuccio
Associate Editor

MUDDLED THINKING

My mother and father **hate** me. They love my sister more. They're always buying her things, like **glasses** and **braces on her teeth** and **corrective shoes**. An' they never buy me **nothin'**.

SELECTIVE SERVICE

9

IT'S WHAT'S UP FRONT THAT COUNTS

Honey, what a terrible day I had. I'm driving the car, I get to the intersection just as the amber light turns red. Then this nut, too impatient to wait for the green light, comes racing out, sideswiping me, putting a dent in the right fender, giving me a whiplash and spraining my wrist.

11

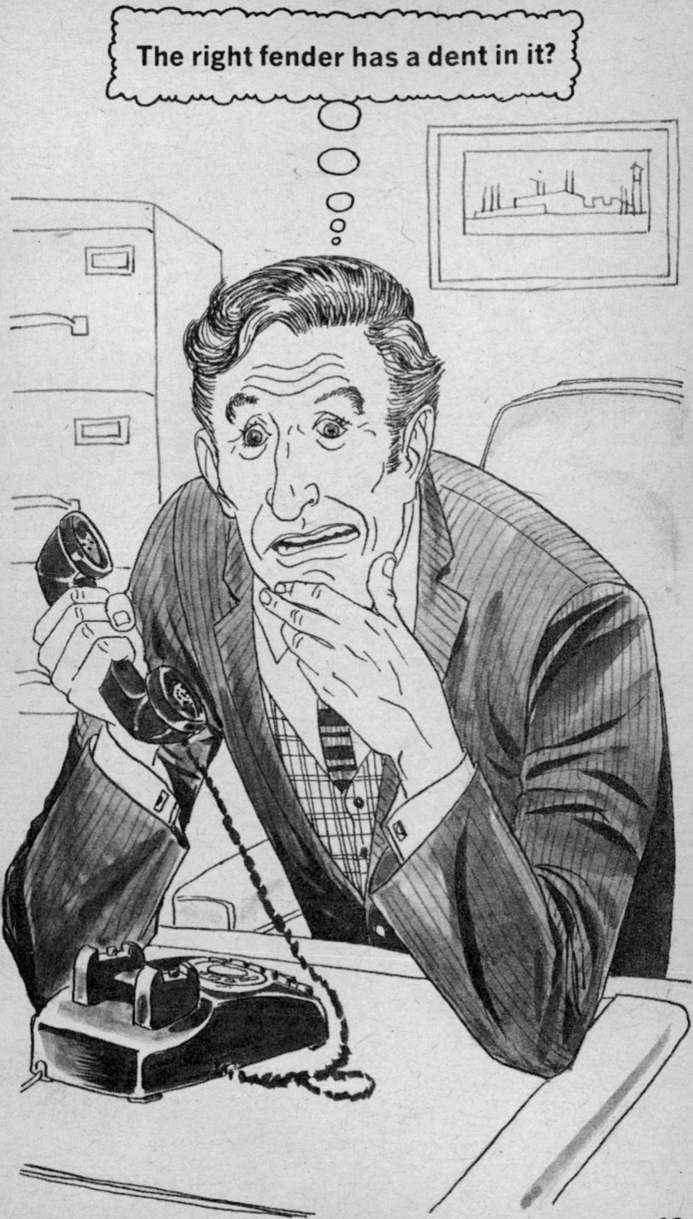
The right fender has a dent in it?

SOUND OFF

15

17

POUND CAKE

Oh boy, does that chocolate cake look delicious. I gotta have some . . . but I can't. If my wife were here, she'd say it's fattening.

19

LOVE FINDS A WAY

21

22

23

THE BURNING QUESTION

Gee, those poor women. Their apartment house is on fire and they had to get out in a hurry in the middle of the night. I can just imagine what horrible thoughts are going through their minds right now.

PLAN A-HEAD

LOVE IS PATERNAL

31

33

VOX POP

35

37

A GROWING PAIN

41

43

BRUSH OFF

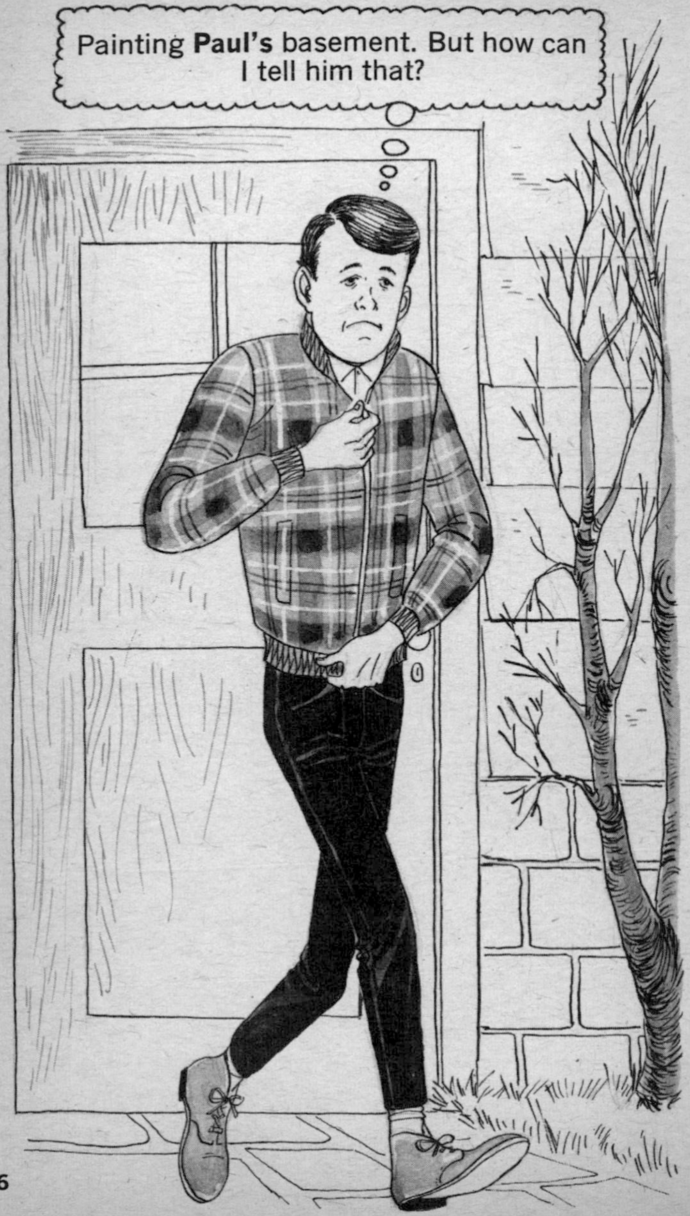
Painting **Paul's** basement. But how can I tell him that?

THE YEAHS HAVE IT

Good, they're coming back. I'm glad my son made friends with Bruce. Both his parents are college graduates, and I barely got through high school. I hope they don't think we're too far beneath them.

CLASS DISTINCTION

DOCTOR H.
SARATOGA

54

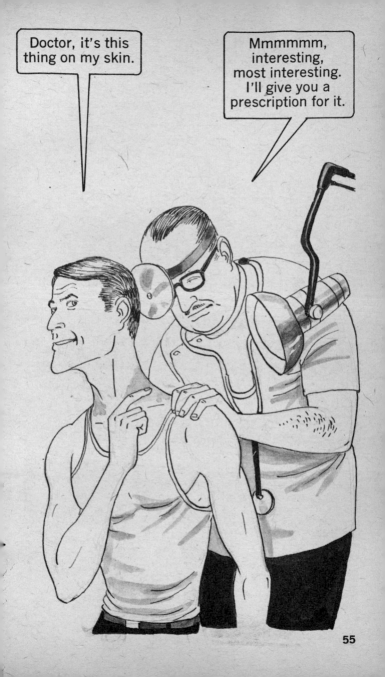

KID NAPPING

59

SEEN BUT NOT HURT

63

SLIGHT OF HAND

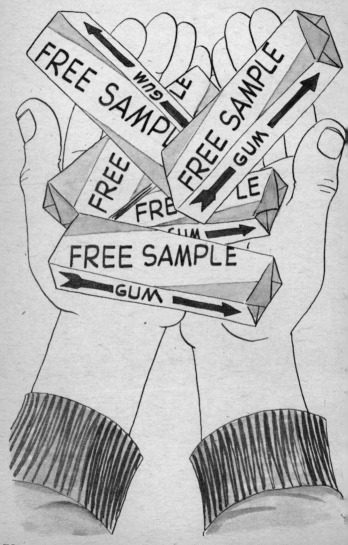

SOCIAL THINKING

NAME DROPPER

FOOT IN MOUTH DISEASE

If there's anything I can't stand,
it's an embarrassing silence.

If there's anything I can't stand, it's an embarrassing conversation.

CURLING IRONY

BRIDE AND BROOM

GET UNACQUAINTED

89

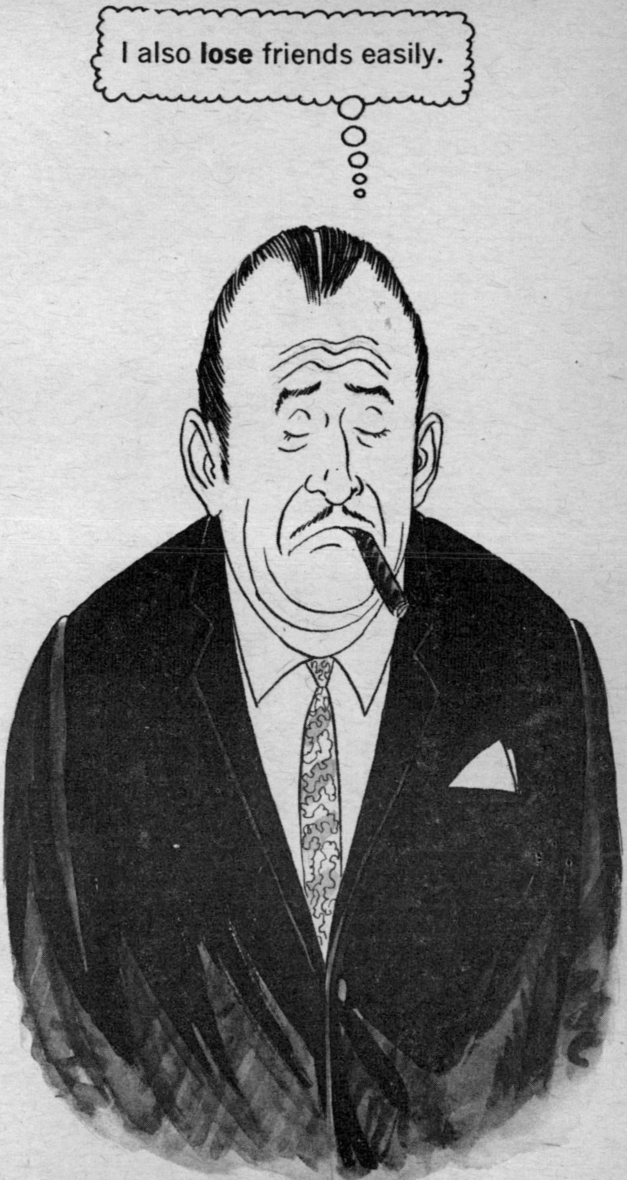
I also **lose** friends easily.

PARTY PEPPER

Look at Regina, she's a true **extrovert,** a real **outgoing** person.

I'll say, and she's so popular. Anytime there's a party, she's the first one they invite.

95

DON'T COME AS YOU ARE

SENSUAL THINKING

SWITCH HITTER

LINE - O - TYPE

HAREM SCAREM'

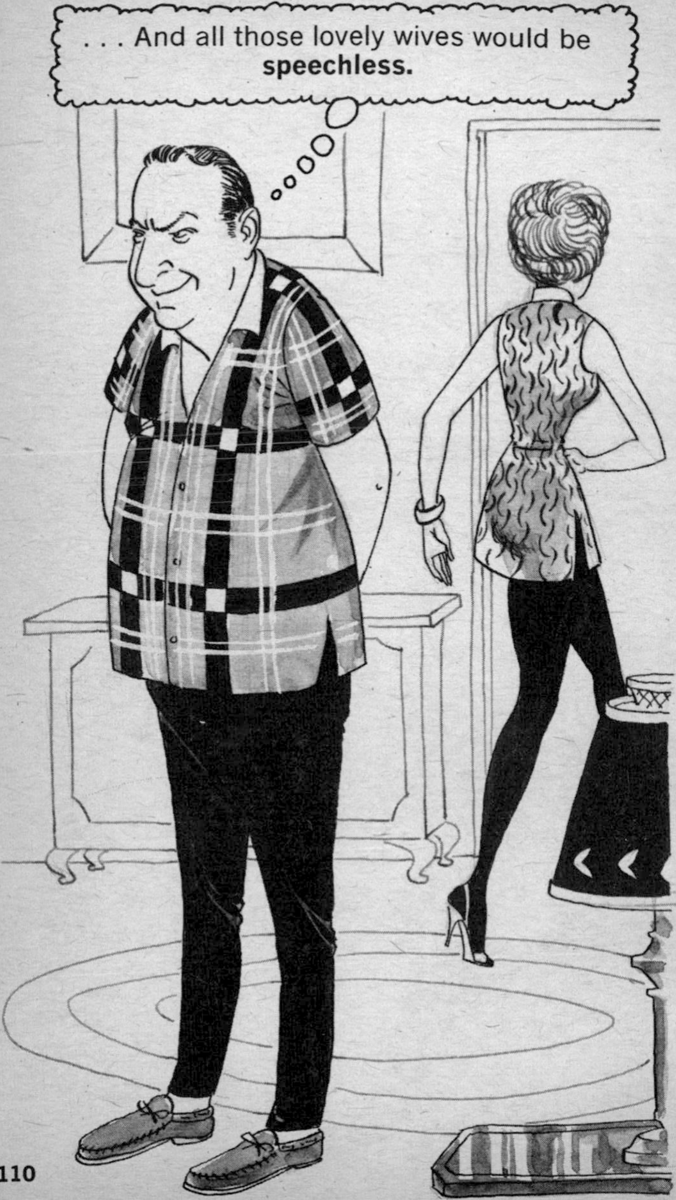
. . . And all those lovely wives would be **speechless.**

WIN, PLACE AND SHOW

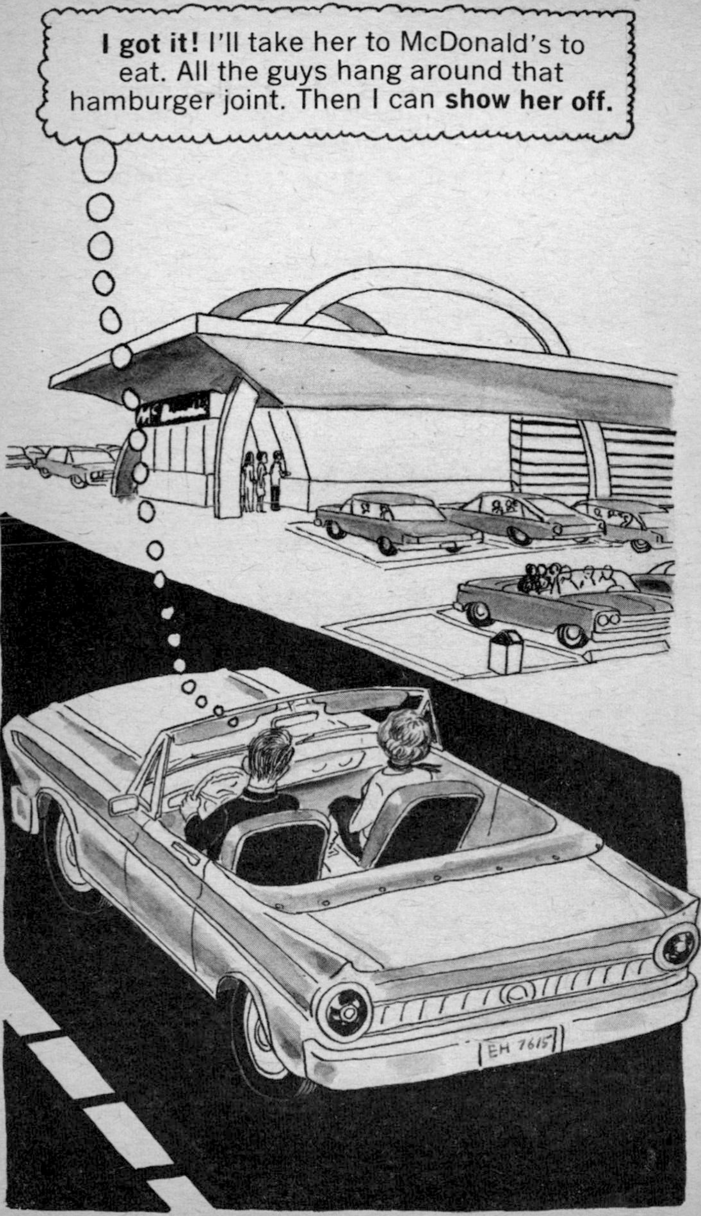
I got it! I'll take her to McDonald's to eat. All the guys hang around that hamburger joint. Then I can **show her off.**
EH 7615

Imagine taking me to a cheap hamburger joint. That's the last time this slob will be seen with me.

THE NOSE KNOWS

Look at those girls wearing bikinis. They are teasingly hiding what in our society is considered **sexy.** In primitive societies, women go around with nothing on but body paint. Yet their men aren't in a constant state of passion.

As I understand it, in Japan, it's the **back of a woman's neck** that's supposed to drive men wild.

117

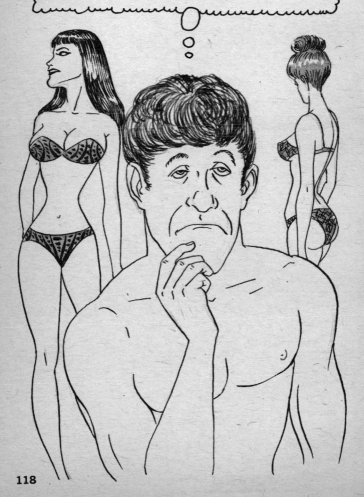

Furthermore, **nose jobs** would no longer consist of **reducing** the size but rather **enlarging** it with **silicone.** And women, to show modesty, would teasingly wear **nose bras.** Small nosed women would wear padded ones, and young girls would wear **training** nose bras.

PHILOSOPHICAL THINKING

PUTTING DESCARTES BEFORE THE HORSE

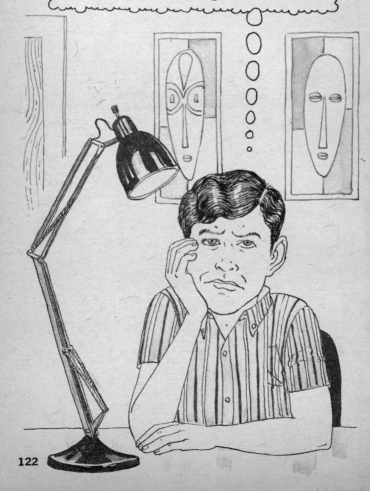

Come to think about it, how do I know anything? Is everything really as it seems to be? How do I know I'm actually me? Maybe I'm just a bad dream somebody is having.

LOVE MAKES THE WORLD GO FLAT

The trouble with this world is that there isn't enough **love** in it.

127

129

THERE'S THE RIB

Boy, have I got hang-ups, and it's all because of my mother! Boy, has she got hang-ups. It's like one person infects another.

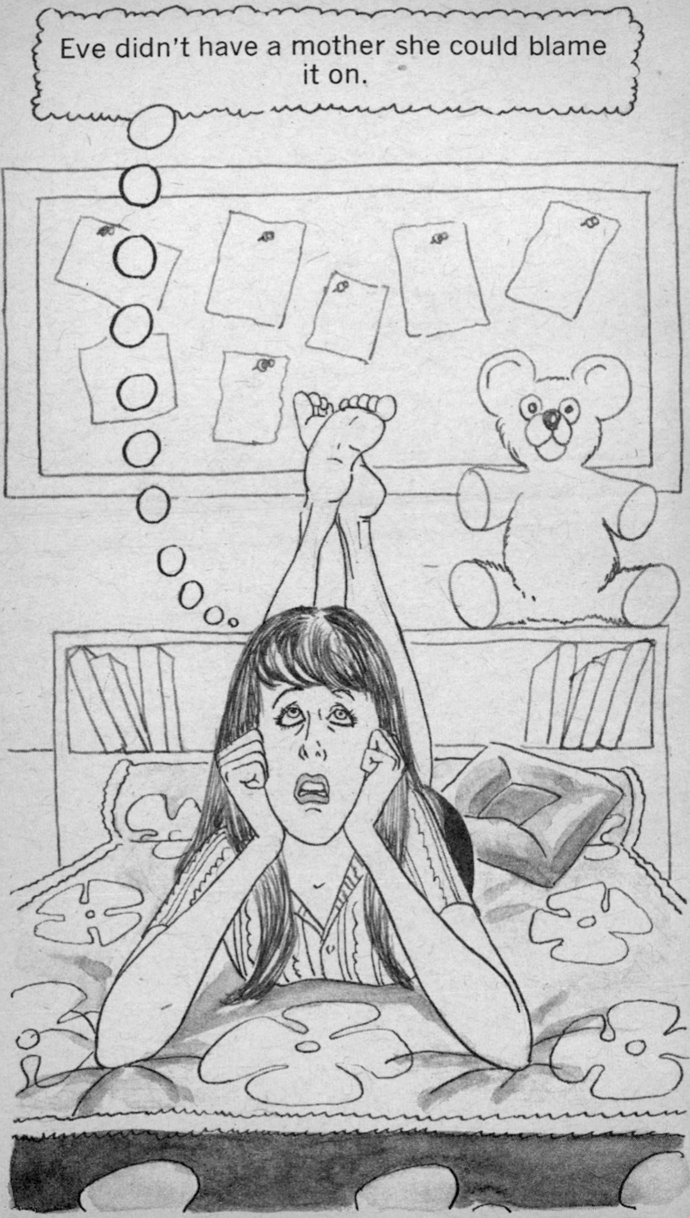
Eve didn't have a mother she could blame it on.

TURN-ABOUT IS FAIR PLAY

That should keep him off my back for a couple of hours. Especially with the complicated mess the world is in, he'll probably never figure it out.

135

GOODNESS KNOWS

How do I **know** there's a **God?** I never **saw** Him. And another thing, who **made** God? And who made the **maker** of God? And what was there **before** the beginning? And where does the universe **end?** And what's on the **other side?**

INSECT CONTROL

HYPOCRITICAL THINKING

SUNNY DISPOSITION

They're probably all criticizing me for spending most of the day just sunning myself while my husband works so hard. As it happens, I'm doing it for **him.** This way I'm attractive and healthy-looking for my mate.

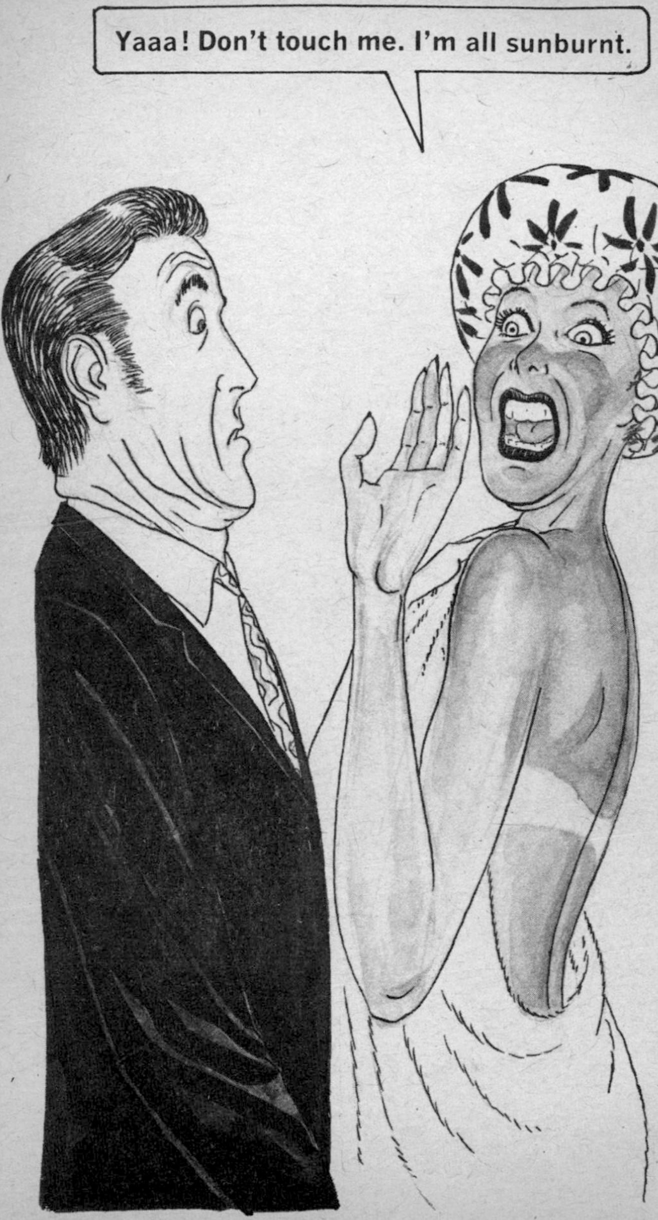
Yaaa! Don't touch me. I'm all sunburnt.

BUDDY SYSTEM

151

THE JOKER IS MILD

Hey, I heard this gag. A man asks his wife if she knows Beethoven. So she says, "Sure I do, I saw him just this morning on the A bus going down Main Street." So he says **"Stupid,** if you don't know what you're talking about then **shut up!** You're only making a fool of yourself. Anybody knows that the **A Bus doesn't** go down Main Street."

Listen how loud Jerry is laughing. Ha, Ha, that gag really broke him up.

FEAT OF CLAY

I mean it.

Look, I'm an ordinary guy, no better, no worse than anyone else. I have my faults, my pettiness, my jealousies like any other mortal.

So don't go building me up to something I can't live up to.

That's another quality about you that I love, your **modesty.**

THE CUSTOMER IS ALWAYS RIGHTEOUS

You gotta watch these **thieving** waiters like hawks. I added up these figures and he deliberately **overcharged** me. **look at that!**

159

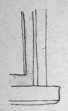

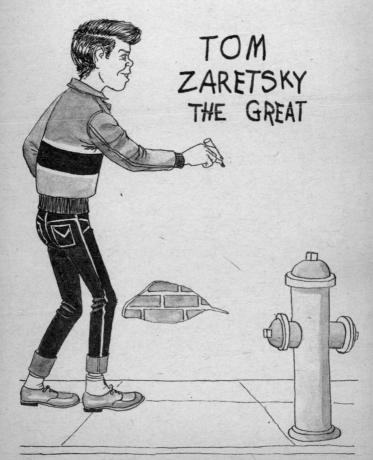

TOM
ZARETSKY
THE GREAT

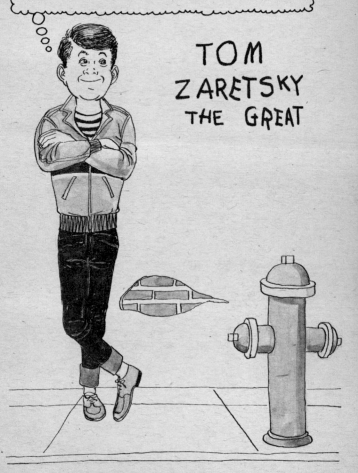

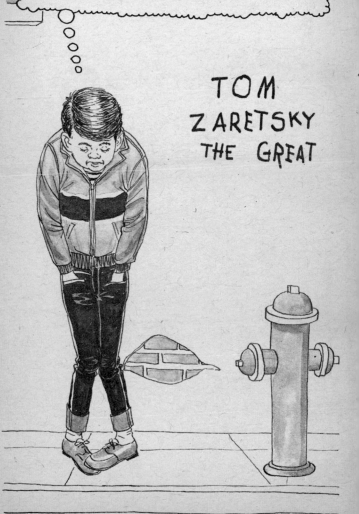

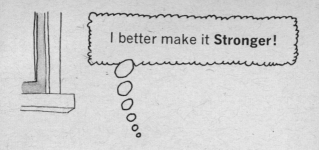

LAUNDROMATE

176

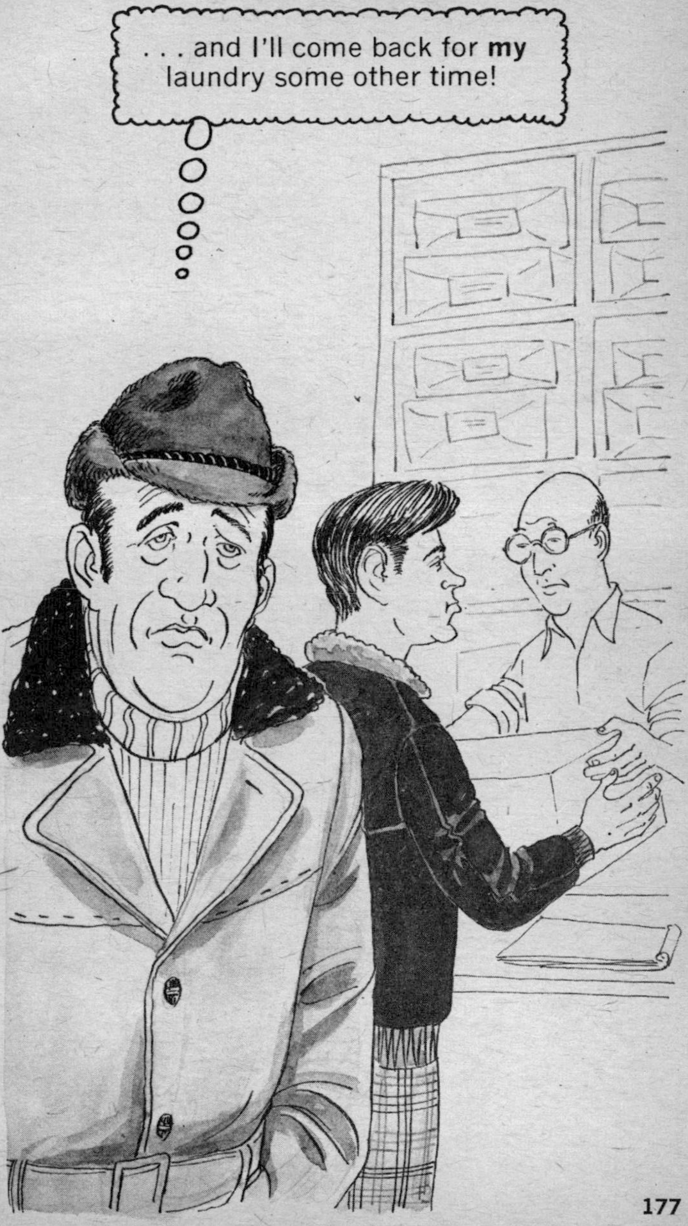
. . . and I'll come back for **my** laundry some other time!

BEGGARS CAN BE LOSERS

PALM READER

184

SUNDAY KIND OF LOVE

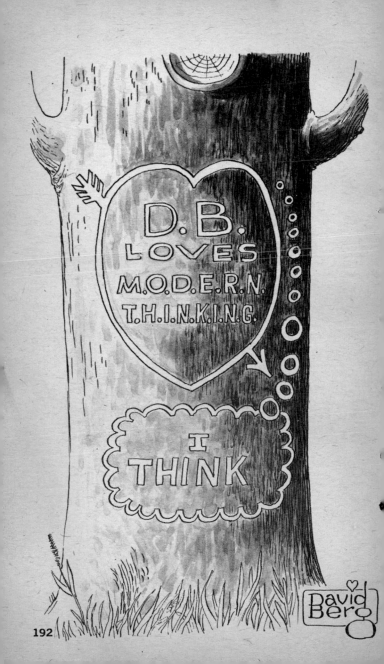